Swim, Shark, Swim!

Dom Conlon

Illustrations Anastasia Izlesou

GRAFFEG

Swim, Shark, Swim!
Published in Great Britain in 2021 by Graffeg Limited.

Written by Dom Conlon copyright © 2021.
Illustrated by Anastasia Izlesou copyright © 2021.
Designed and produced by Graffeg copyright © 2021.

Graffeg, 24 Stradey Park Business Centre,
Mwrwg Road, Llangennech, Llanelli,
Carmarthenshire, SA14 8YP, Wales, UK.
Tel: 01554 824000. www.graffeg.com.

ISBN 9781914079054

1 2 3 4 5 6 7 8 9

Swim, Shark, Swim!

Dom Conlon
Illustrations Anastasia Izlesou

This book belongs to:

_____

_____

_____

Blue sun in sunken skies
the sea sharpens to the shape
of Shark off the west coast
of Australia.

With black tips on his fins
and the space between stars in his eyes
ask – where is he going,
ask – what does he want?

This reef-watcher, jewel-guarder
will tell you he's lost –
lost in a place where the land pours
sand from an outstretched hand.

He's too close to shore
and when a boat drops a net
like the lines on a globe
he opens a tunnel
of bubbles and light and
swim, Shark, SWIM!

Could this be Shark's home
where African penguins
plunge through clouds of silvery fish
and cape fur seals spin
flip-happy hoops?

No. Not this.

This is where the tiger shark lives.
With fading stripes and well-worn teeth,
he's hungry for the humpback whale
which rolls like a tyre ready to pop.

So Shark speeds away
through this saltwater world.

From the South to the North Atlantic,
Shark slips through a handshake
of continents to where the whitetip shark
farms for food day and night
with pilot fish and remora by her side.

But finding food here is hard
and Shark's getting hungry,

so he opens a tunnel
of bubbles and light and

swim, Shark, SWIM!

He swims in a whizz and a fizz
past Morocco and Spain
to the wing-tipped waves of Wales.

A tunnel-mouthed basking shark
preys from above
whilst an angel shark
lies on the ocean floor.

These are cathedral-cold waters
and Shark bows his head
and turns around.

Patrolling North American waters
like a siren at night,
a blue shark chases octopus and squid.

Shark wants to join in
but Blue's smile is fierce,

so he opens a tunnel
of bubbles and light and
swim, Shark, SWIM!

Across to where mangroves
net the tides with their roots.

This is where young lemon sharks live,
growing in their nursery's safe shallows.

They are sandy-sinkers, ocean-drinkers
and our shark could swing by to say hi
but a hurricane winds above like a clock
and Shark has no time to waste

so he opens a tunnel
of bubbles and light and

swim, Shark, SWIM!

To South America,
where warm waters snake into cold
and Shark's keen nose catches the scent
of a hammerhead shark
hoovering the seabed for stingrays
which hide beneath chameleon cloaks.

But Shark, these
waters aren't yours
so leave Hammerhead be
and be on your way.

Be on your way as night drips into the sea
and a bottlenose dolphin leaps to the Moon.

Shark can leap too, though he's wary because
a human bobs up and down.

Mammal and fish – here in the Pacific
it's a meeting of worlds
but Shark misses his home
and has miles more to go

so he opens a tunnel
of bubbles and light and
swim, Shark, SWIM!

To the emerald sparkle of Californian waters
where a great white shark slips into view,
slicing wolf-eels from forests of kelp
like the sea's ancient spear.

Even sharks feel fear
and it's best to stay out of her way,

but Great White catches sight
of Shark who takes flight so
speed, Shark, SPEED!

Speed out of reach of
Great White's sharp teeth
and speed through the waves
like a rocket of flesh.

Speed, Shark, speed,
past the coast of Hawaii
where green sea turtles dive
and manta rays flip black and white.

Speed, Shark, speed
to the Great Barrier Reef –
a chorus of coral
singing colours in the sea.

Home and happy, our shark belongs
with this dark constellation of blacktip reef sharks.
Together they feed,
helping the reefs to live and thrive so

hunt, Shark, HUNT!

PACIFIC
OCEAN

NORTH ATLANTIC
OCEAN

INDIAN
OCEAN

SOUTH ATLANTIC
OCEAN

31

Shark Facts

Swim, Shark, Swim! shows the imaginary journey of a blacktip reef shark travelling around the world. The blacktip wouldn't usually migrate in this way but we're letting him – just this once – in order to introduce us to many other sharks and marine life.

Sharks are beautiful creatures who help keep the ocean in balance. If the numbers of one type of marine animal become too great then they can do a lot of harm and reduce the diversity of animal and plant life in our seas. By hunting, sharks keep those numbers down.

Climate change is causing the oceans to get warmer and more acidic. This is causing a great deal of harm and is one of the reasons the beautiful coral reefs are turning white and dying.

Here are some of the other sharks, sea life and sights he sees along the way.

African penguin
Lives in the waters around South Africa and is now endangered.

Angel shark
A flattened shark which hunts by lying on sandy seabeds and ambushing its prey.

Basking shark
The second largest shark in the world, it has a mouth which is 1m across, prefers colder water and eats plankton.

Blacktip reef shark
The shark in this story is a blacktip, which likes to hunt in groups. The blacktip is a member of the requiem shark species and prefers warmer waters.

Blue shark
Lives in all but the coldest waters and sometimes hunts in groups to catch bigger prey.

Bottlenose dolphin
Intelligent and friendly, these creatures use sound to discover the size and location of their food.

Cape fur seal
These are the largest seal species and can sleep on land or in the water.

Great Barrier Reef
A large area of coral off the coast of Australia. Many parts are fading, turning from beautiful colours to ghostly white, because of the effect humans are having on the sea.

Great white shark
The largest hunting fish on the planet, they can swim as fast as 15mph and have 300 very sharp teeth, but rarely hurt humans.

Green sea turtles
Large and heavy, these eat sea plants, live in coastal waters and are endangered.

Hammerhead shark
Their wide heads help them to make quick turns, and they can even get a tan!

Humans
Sharks are in danger from other sharks, crocodiles and even dolphins, but humans pose the greatest danger. Over 100 million sharks are killed each year by hunters.

Kelp
A type of seaweed which grows like underwater trees in shallow parts of the ocean.

Lemon shark
These sharks are a little bit yellow, which helps camouflage them against the sandy floor of shallow waters where the pups are born.

Mangroves
Tropical trees which can grow in salty water and can store a huge amount of carbon dioxide, making them very important in fighting climate change.

Oceanic whitetip shark
Keeping mostly to tropical seas, this shark is fierce and usually travels alone but is sometimes seen with smaller fish like remora or pilot fish.

Octopus
Very intelligent and very bendy, they can use the suckers on their limbs to open clams and move objects, and they can shoot black ink to help hide themselves in order to escape.

Plankton
Tiny living creatures which mostly float through the ocean currents.

Stingrays
Spend most of their time hiding from sharks but also have a venom which can be deadly to humans.

Dom Conlon

Dom Conlon is a double Carnegie-nominated poet and author whose work is guided by nature and the stars. He's written poetry and picture books, fact and fiction — sometimes all in the same book.

Nicola Davies said *Leap, Hare, Leap!* is 'full of the lushness of summer'. Chris Riddell said *This Rock That Rock* contained 'words and pictures that are quite simply out of this world'. Dallas Campbell said *Meet Matilda Rocket Builder* is 'a must read for all aspiring rocket scientists'.

Dom hopes to inspire everyone to read and write poetry. Discover more at www.domconlon.com

Anastasia Izlesou

Anastasia Izlesou is a multidisciplinary illustrator and designer from the UK. Using a mix of digital and traditional media, she creates vibrant work full of bold natural elements.

Her inspirations range from natural sciences, literature and folklore to everyday items and objects of kitsch.

The White Hare, published by Graffeg, was Anastasia's first published book, followed by *Leap, Hare, Leap!*, the first title in this Wild Wanderers series.